TheNewDivas

London / New Yo[...] [...]rlin / Madrid / Tokyo

Published by
WISE PUBLICATIONS
8/9 Frith Street, London, W1D 3JB, England.

Exclusive distributors:
MUSIC SALES LIMITED
Distribution Centre, Newmarket Road,
Bury St Edmunds, Suffolk, IP33 3YB, England.
MUSIC SALES PTY LIMITED
120 Rothschild Avenue, Rosebery, NSW 2018, Australia.

Order No. AM983796
ISBN 1-84609-242-6

Cover designed by Michael Bell Design.
Cover photographs courtesy of
Michael Benabib: Retna/Bernhard Kuhmstedt: Retna/
LFI/Statia Molewski: Retna/Rex Features.
Printed in the United Kingdom.

www.musicsales.com

The Closest Thing To Crazy

Words & Music by Mike Batt

C♯m
C♯m/B
A
4fr
How can hap - pi - ness feel so wrong?
It's so ea - sy to break a heart.
G♯m
B9
E
B7
4fr
How can mi - se - ry feel so sweet?
It's so ea - sy to close your eyes.
E
B/F♯
E/G♯
E
How can you let me watch you sleep then
How can you treat me like a child yet
A6
A
E
break my dreams the way you do?
like a child I yearn for you?

C♯m
4fr
C♯m/B
A
How can I have got in so deep?
How can a - ny - one feel so wild?
G♯m
4fr
B9
E
B7
Why did I fall in love with you?
How can a - ny - one feel so blue?
This is the
3
E
C♯m9
clos - est thing to cra - zy I have ev - er been.
Feel - ing
F♯m6
B6
B
twen - ty two, act - ing sev - en - teen.
This is the
3

E
C♯m9
near - est thing to cra - zy I have ev - er known. I was
F♯m7
Am(maj7)
nev - er cra - zy on my own and
E
C♯m
4fr
A
3
now I know that there's a link be - tween the two.
C
E
C♯m
4fr
Be - ing close to cra - zi - ness and

1.
B
E
B7/F♯
be - ing close to you.
E/G♯
Asus4
Am
E
2.
E
C♯m
4fr
A
Bsus4
2fr
And be - ing close to
rit.
E
C♯m7
4fr
Aadd9
Bsus4
2fr
E
you.
And be - ing close to you.
8vb

Again

Words & Music by Faith Evans, Venus Dobson & Jerry Harris

Dadd9
4fr
('cos I'm strug - gl - ing, and bro - ken hearts to fan - cy cars, ooh,
Amaj7
5fr
C♯m7
4fr
yeah.) And ev - en though my mo - ney changed I tried my best to stay the same,
Dadd9
4fr
Bm9
7fr
E9
6fr
but you know with my mon - ey my prob - lems came.
Amaj7
5fr
C♯m7
4fr
If I had to do it all a - gain, I

Dadd9
4fr
would - n't take a - way the rain, 'cos I know it made me who I
Amaj7
5fr
C♯m7
4fr
am. If I had to do it all a - gain, I've
Dadd9
4fr
Bm7
7fr
E11
7fr
learned so much from my mis - takes, that's how I know he's watch - in' me.
1.
Amaj7
5fr
C♯m7
4fr
In A. - T. - L. I caught a case and the me - di - a tried to say

Dadd9
4fr
Dmaj7
5fr
I had a ha - bit, I could-n't man - age and I'm throw-ing my life a - way.
Amaj7
5fr
C♯m7
4fr
But ev-'ry-thing ain't what it seems just be-cause it's on t - v,
Dadd9
4fr
Bm9
7fr
E11
7fr
3
'cos they spec - u - late and ex - ag - ge - rate for a bet - ter sto - ry.
2.
Amaj7
5fr
C♯m7
4fr
No - bo - dy knows what life may bring, might

Dadd9
4fr
Dmaj7
5fr
make you hap - py, it might make you sad some-times,
Amaj7
5fr
C#m7
4fr
yeah. (But I know there's a rea - son for ev - 'ry - thing.) that's why I
Dadd9
4fr
Bm9
7fr
E11
7fr
keep be- liev - ing what-ev-er's meant to be is gon - na
Amaj7
5fr
C#m7
4fr
be. (If I had to do it all a - gain, I
(1° only)
Lead vocal ad lib.

Dadd9
4fr
would - n't take a - way the rain, 'cos I know it made me who I
Amaj7
5fr
C#m7
4fr
am. If I had to do it all a - gain, I've
Dadd9
4fr
Bm7
7fr
E11
7fr
Repeat ad lib. to fade
learned so much from my mis - takes, that's how I know he's watch - in' me.)

Crazy Chick

Words & Music by Fitzgerald Scott, Wirlie Morris & Sarah Buras

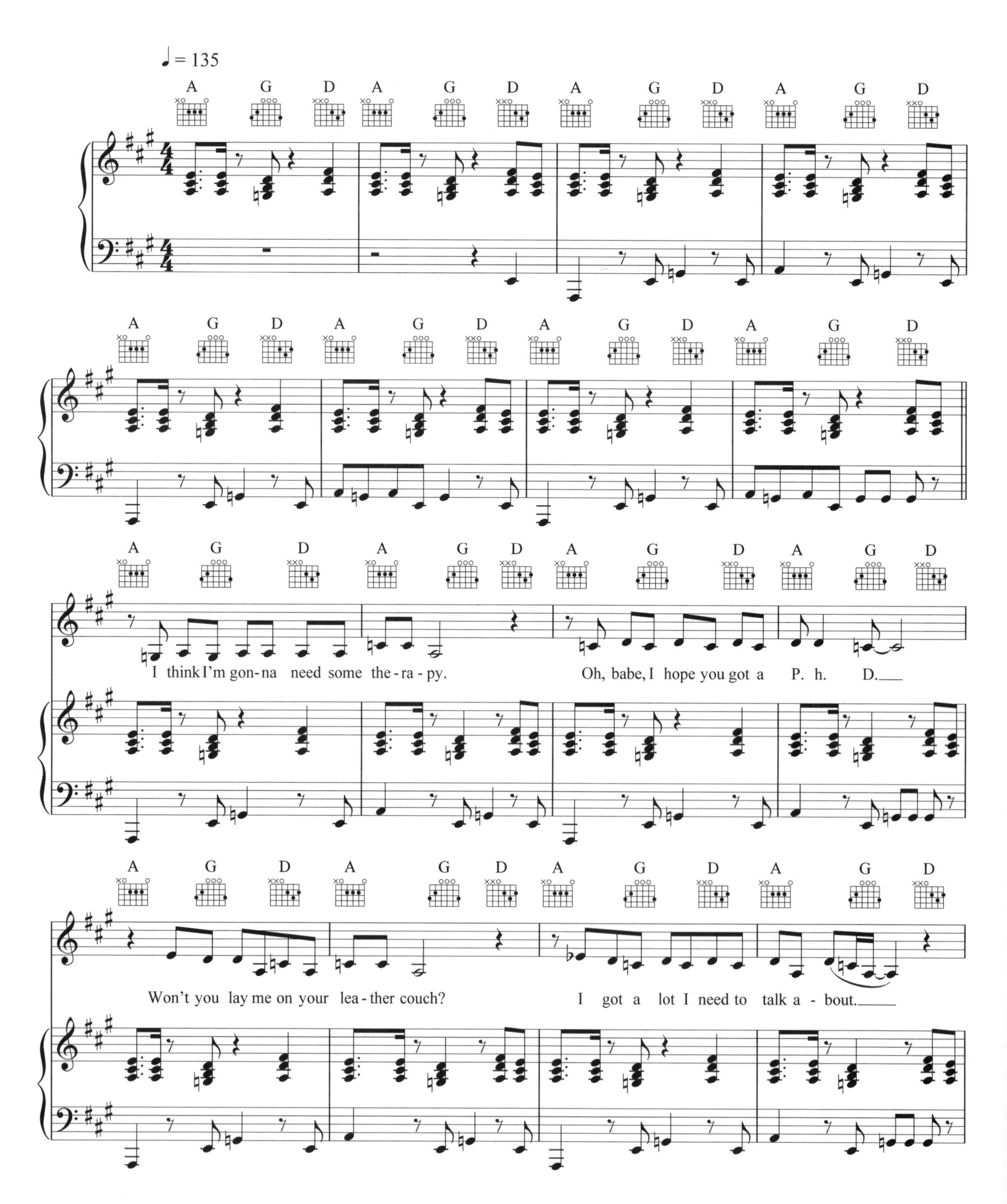

A G D A G D A G D
I think I'm cra - zy, think I'm stu - pid, must have lost my mind, won - d'ring what I'm think-ing lov - ing
A G D A G D A G D
you 'cos boy if you were mine, I'd real - ly go in - sane, you'd be my fav - 'rite thing,
A G D A7 Fmaj7 C
I'd go bal - lis - tic, yeah you're ma - king me a cra - zy chick! You're driv - ing me to in - san - i - ty,
Dm7 A7 Fmaj7
all the things you do, you make me come un - glued, I just can't help my - self:

C
D7
E9
A
G
D
3fr
5fr
6fr
I need pro - fes - sio - nal help,
help, I need pro - fes - sio - nal help.
N.C.
You've real - ly done it this time,
you know you've twis - ted my mind, you've got me act - ing like a whacked out chick. So I
A9
12fr
won't be res - pon - si - ble 'cos I'm real - ly not lo - gi - cal. No I won't be to blame, you know I'm

A G D A G D
real - ly not sane.
I think I'm cra - zy, think I'm stu - pid, must have lost my mind,
A G D A G D A G D
won - der what I'm think - ing lov - ing you 'cos boy if you were mine, I'd real - ly go in - sane,
To Coda
A G D A G D A G D
you'd be my fav - 'rite thing, I'd go bal - lis - tic, yeah you're ma - king me a cra - zy chick!
Fmaj7 C Dm7 A7
3fr 5fr 5fr
You're driv - ing me to in - san - i - ty, all the things you do, you make me come un - glued,

Fmaj7
C
D7
E9
I just can't help my - self: I need pro-fes-sion-al help, help.
Dm7
Cmaj7
B♭maj7
Am7
Can't get you out of my head, so let me just con - fess,
Dm7
Cmaj7
E♭maj9
D.S. al Coda
for those kis-ses ba-by, for your love, you drive me cra-zy, I can't get e-nough, no!
Coda
A G D A G D A G D A G D
ma - kingme a cra-zy chick! You're driv-ing me to in-san - i - ty, all the things you do,

A
G
D
Fmaj7
C
3fr
D7
5fr
you make me come un - glued, I just can't help my - self: I need pro-fes-sion-al help, help.
E9
6fr
Fmaj7
C
3fr
Dm7
5fr
You're driv-ing me to in-san - i - ty, all the things you do,
A7
5fr
Fmaj7
C
3fr
you make me come un - glued, I just can't help my - self: I need pro - fes-sion - al help,
1.
D7
5fr
E9
6fr
help, I need pro - fes-sion-al help.
2.
D7
5fr
E9
6fr
rall.
N.C.
A9
4fr
help, I need help.

Don't Cha Wanna Ride

Words & Music by Desmond Child, Steve Greenberg, Eugene Record, Michael Mangini, Joss Stone, Betty Wright & William Sanders

Dmaj7
5fr
G/A
7fr
feel like you just might be some-one who I could get in - to. But I
girls say you're hard to please, but I think that I got just what you need. Get your
Dmaj7
5fr
G/A
7fr
nev - er seem to catch your eye, and it's been bug-gin' me why I ev-en try, still, you're
face out of the mir - ror, then may-be you could con-si - der this
Dmaj7
5fr
G/A
7fr
some-one I'd like to get to know, is there room for me in your one - man show?
girl who's knock-in' right at your door make room for me in your one - man show.
N.C.
Dmaj7
5fr
G/A
7fr
A car this fine don't pass your way ev-'ry day, don't

Dmaj7
5fr
G/A
7fr
cha wan-na ride ba - by, don't cha wan-na ride ba - by? A
car this fine don't pass your way ev-'ry day, don't cha wan-na ride ba - by?
1.
Time is slip - ping by, by, by by, slip-ping
2.
by. 2. I was by, by, by

G/A
Dmaj7
G/A
7fr
5fr
by,
oh.
Dmaj7
G/A
Dmaj7
I know you've got the Hum-mer for the sum-
G/A
Dmaj7
-mer ba - by, but I got your num - ber ba - by, I got your
G/A
Dmaj7
G/A
num-ber ba - by. I know where you live, I know all 'bout your crib, but do

Dmaj7
5fr
G/A
7fr
you, do you, do you, do you know that they can't give you what I
give? No Lord.
N.C.
Ooh.
A
car this fine don't pass your way ev - 'ry day, don't
cha wan - na ride ba - by?

Dmaj7
5fr
G/A
7fr
car this fine don't pass your way ev - 'ry day, don't
Dmaj7
5fr
G/A
7fr
cha wan-na ride ba - by?
A
Dmaj7
5fr
G
5fr
car this fine don't pass your way ev - 'ry day, don't
Dmaj7
5fr
G
5fr
cha wan-na ride ba - by?

Everytime

Words & Music by Britney Spears & Annette Stamatelatos

B♭sus2
E♭sus2
Cm
3fr
Gm
3fr
stran - gers when
our love is strong,
I see clear.
What have I done?
At night I pray
*
E♭sus2
Gm
3fr
E♭sus2
why car - ry on with - out me?
You seem to move un - ea - sy.
that soon your face will fade a - way.
E♭
B♭
Cm
3fr
Ev - 'ry - time I try to fly I fall, with - out my wings
Gm7
3fr
A♭
4fr
Fm6
I feel so small. I guess I need you ba - by.

E♭
B♭
Cm
3fr
And ev - 'ry - time I see you in my dreams I see your face,
Gm7
3fr
A♭
4fr
Fm6
To Coda
it's haunt - ing me. I guess I need you ba - by.
1.
E♭sus2
B♭sus2
E♭sus2
Cm
3fr
8va
Harp
2.
Cm
3fr
A♭
4fr
Fm
I may have made it rain.

G
Cm
3fr
A♭
4fr
Please for - give me.
And my weak - ness caused you pain
Fm
G
rit.
D.S. al Coda
and this song's my sor - ry.
8va
Coda
E♭
B♭
Cm
3fr
Gm7
3fr
A♭
4fr
Fm6
E♭
8va

Feel Good Time

Words & Music by Beck, William Orbit & Jay Ferguson

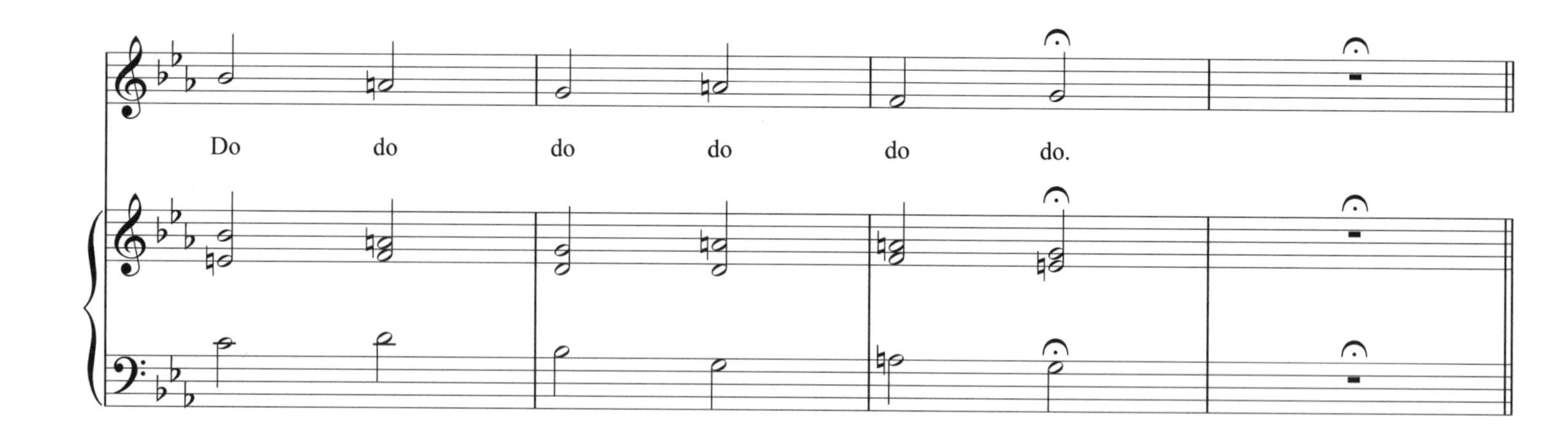

N.C.
C
B♭
F
E♭
1. We go where we like we got ov - er - time, we get paid to rat - tle our chains.
2. We know how to play, par - ty ev - 'ry - day, make our de - so - la - tion look plain.
We go in the back, paint our mon - ey black, spend it on the
Rid - ing in a rut 'till the pow - er's cut, we don't ev - en
e - ne - my.
have a good name.
Sleep - in' in the church, rid - in'

E♭
C
B♭
F
in the dirt, put a ban - ner ov - er my grave.
Make a bo - dy work, make a beg - gar hurt, sell me some - thin' big and un - tamed.
Now our time, real good time.
Now our time,

E♭
C
B♭
F
E♭
real good time.
Now our time,
C
E♭
C
B♭
F
real good time.
E♭
N.C.
Hey
be all
mine.

Do do do do do.
do
Do do do do do
C
B♭
F
E♭
do.
Now our time,
real good time.
Now our time,

E♭
C
B♭
F
E♭
real good time.
Now our time,
C
B♭
F
E♭
C
B♭
F
real good time.
E♭
C
B♭
F
E♭
Feel good, real good, it's the
C
B♭
F
E♭
C
same old same
Real good, feel

E♭
C
E♭
good, don't got no more brains.
C
B♭
F
E♭
C
E♭
Feel good, real good, it's the same old same.
C
B♭
F
E♭
C
B♭
F
Real good, feel good, don't got no more brains
E♭
N.C.
hey be all mine.

The Game Is Won

Words & Music by Michael Peden, Lucie Silvas, Judie Tzuke & Graham Kearns

C
Gm7
3fr
jump right in but now I'm not so sure. If I put
be a - fraid of what I can't con - trol 'cause what -
E♭
F
two and two to - geth - er oh, will I still get four?
- ev - er's round the cor - ner I will take it all.
G
G/F
C/E
E♭
And I know where I be - long, but I'm still break - ing through,
G
G/F
E♭
D
some - times I get it wrong but I'm keep - ing it true.

G F/A E♭ F
If ev-'ry-thing is how it should be, then ev-'ry-thing will come,
G F/A E♭ F
when it gets here I'll be rea - dy, oh,
G F/A E♭ F
if it's just de - ter - mi - na - tion ev-'ry-thing will come,
E♭ D
To Coda
1.
G G/F C/E E♭
and the game's al-rea-dy won.
2. They say you

2.
G
G/F
C/E
E♭
Be - liev - ing in my - self can't be wrong. No.
I'm wait - ing for my time in the sun, yeah, oh.
Be - liev - ing in my - self can't be wrong, oh, oh,
I'm wait - ing for my time in the sun. Oh.
D.S. al Coda

Coda
G
F/A
E♭/B♭
F/C
Be-liev-ing in my-self can't be wrong.
Vocal ad lib.
G
F/A
E♭/B♭
F/A
Be-liev-ing in my-self can't be wrong.
G
F/A
E♭/B♭
F/A
E♭
D
Be-liev-ing in my-self can't be wrong,
and the game's al-rea-dy won.
rit.
G
G/F
C/E
E♭
F
G
Yeah, ooh.
Mm,
mm.

Leave (Get Out)

Words & Music by Carsten Schack, Kenneth Karlin, Alexander Cantrall & Phillip White

Gm7
Dm7
Csus4
C
B♭
10fr
5fr
3fr
— to me? —— You tell me how we're gon - na be — to - geth - er al - ways. —
— the truth? —— How could you e - ver be — so cold? ——
— Hope you know that when it's late — at night — I hold on to my pil -
— To go be - hind my back and call — my friend, — boy, you must have gone and bumped —
- low tight, — and think of how you prom - ised me — for - ev - er.
— your head, — be - cause you
1° only
2° only
left a num - ber on — your phone. ——
(I ne - ver thought that an - y - one...)
(So now af - ter all is said — and done...)

Csus4
C
B♭
Gm7
Dm7
make me feel this way, uh. (Now that you're here, boy, all I want...) is
may-be I'm the one to blame, (To think that you could be the one.) Well, it
Csus4
C
B♭
Gm
Gsus2
Dsus4
Dm
just the chance to say, hey....
didn't work out that way, hey.
Get out! (Leave!) Right now,
C
B♭maj7
Gm
Gsus2
Dsus4
Dm
Dsus4
it's the end of you and me.
It's too late, (Now!) and I can't wait for
C
Csus4
Gm7
Gm
Gsus2
Dsus4
Dm
you to be gone, 'cos I know
a-bout her (Who?) and I won-der

C
B♭maj7
Gm7
Dm7
3fr
10fr
5fr
(Why?) how I bought all the lies, you said that you would treat me right, but you was
C
Gm7
D♭
3fr
4fr
just a waste of time.
(Waste of time!)
1. I wan - ted you right here with me,
2. I gave up ev - 'ry - thing I had
E♭
6fr
1. F
8fr
but I have no choice, you've got - ta leave
on some - thing that just would - n't last,
be - cause my heart is break - in'
E♭
6fr
2. B♭
6fr
with ev - 'ry word I'm say - 'in.
but I've re - fused to cry,
3
3

C
Gm7
Dm7
8fr
10fr
5fr
no tears will fall from these
eyes.
Csus4
C
Bb
3fr
Uh,
uh,
Get out!
(Get out!
Right now,
Lead vocals ad lib.
(Leave!)
Gm
Gsus2
Dsus4
Dm
Bbmaj7
it's the end of you and me.
It's too late,
and I can't wait for
(Now!)

C
Csus4
Gm7
Gm
Gsus2
Dsus4
Dm
you to be gone, 'cos I know a-bout her and I won-der
(Who?)
C
B♭maj7
Gm7
Dm7
how I bought all the lies, you said that you would treat me right, but you was
(Why?)
C
Gm7
Play 3 times
just a waste of time.
(Waste of time!)
Vocals 1° only
Uh,
Repeat to fade
uh,
uh.

Left Outside Alone

Words & Music by Glen Ballard, Dallas Austin & Anastacia

D5
5fr
G5
3fr
Gm
3fr
A5/G
I don't feel safe,
Ohhh...
Dm
(8vb until chorus)
Left bro-ken, emp-ty, in des-pair,
Gm7
3fr
wan-na breathe, can't find air, thought you were sent from up a-bove, but you and me nev-er had love.

B♭
A
Dm
So much more I have to say, help me find a way.
(loco)
B♭
C
And I won-der if you know how it real-ly feels to be left out-side a-lone
Dm
B♭
when it's cold out here. Well, may-be you should know just how it feels
C
Asus4
A
to be left out-side a-lone, to be left out-side a-lone. I tell you...

B♭
C
Dm
All my life I've been wait - ing for you to bring a fair - y - tale my way,
B♭
C
been liv - ing in a fan - ta - sy with-out mean - ing, it's not o-
3
3
A7sus4
Dm
-kay, I don't feel safe, I need to pray.
Why do you play me like a game? Al-ways some-one else to blame.

Gm7
3fr
B♭
Careless, helpless little man, someday you might understand. There's not much more to say,
A
Dm
but I hope you find a way. Still I wonder if you know
B♭
C
Dm
how it really feels to be left outside alone when it's cold out here.
B♭
C
Well, maybe you should know just how it feels to be left outside alone,

Asus4
A
B♭
to be left out-side a-lone.
I tell you...
All my life I've been wait-
C
Dm
-ing for you to bring a fair-y-tale my way,
been liv-ing in a
B♭
C
A7sus4
fan-ta-sy with-out mean-ing,
it's not o-kay,
I don't feel
Dm
safe,
I need to
pray.
Ohhh...

Gm
3fr
— pray — ohhh... — Hea-ven-ly Fa - ther, oh,
B♭
Asus4
A
Dm
save me. — Ohhh... —
And I won-der if you know —
— how it real-ly feels — to be left out-side a-lone — when it's cold out here. —
C
— Well, may-be you should know — just how it feels — to be left out-side a-lone, —

Asus4
A
B♭
to be left out-side a-lone.
All my life I've been wait-
C
Dm
-ing for you to bring a fair-y-tale my way.
Been liv-ing in a
B♭
C
A7sus4
fan-ta-sy with-out mean-ing, ooh... it's not o-kay,
I don't feel
Dm
Voice echoes to fade
safe, I need to pray.

Love At First Sight

Words & Music by Kylie Minogue, Richard Stannard,
Julian Gallagher, Ash Howes & Martin Harrington

C♭add9 D♭ E♭m
Ev - 'ry - thing went from wrong to right, and the
C♭add9 D♭ E♭m C♭add9
stars came out and filled up the sky. The mu - sic you were play - ing real - ly
To Coda
D♭ E♭m C♭add9 D♭ E♭m
blew my mind. It was love at first sight. 'Cos
C♭maj7 D♭ E♭m C♭maj7
ba - by when I heard you for the first

D♭
E♭m
C♭maj7
D♭
E♭m
time, I knew we were meant to be as
1.
C♭maj7
D♭
E♭m
C♭maj7
one
D♭
E♭m
D♭
E♭m
D♭
E♭m
2.
C♭maj7
D♭
E♭m
one

C♭maj7
D♭
E♭m
Ba - by when I heard you for the first
time, I knew we were meant to be as
one.

D.%. al Coda
D♭
E♭m
C♭maj7
Coda
C♭add9
fr6
first sight. Love at first sight. Love
at first sight. Love,
ooh, it was first love at first sight. 'Cos

C♭maj7
D♭
E♭m
ba - by when I heard you for the first
time, I knew we were meant to be as
1.
one.
2.
one. It was love,

Verse 2:
Was tired of running out of luck,
Thinking 'bout giving up, yeah.
Didn't know what to do,
Then there was you.

And everything went from wrong to right *etc.*

Other Side Of The World

Words & Music by KT Tunstall & Terefe Holmstrom

G
D
Dsus2
Dsus4
Dsus2
the wa - ter.
A
Em7
A
2. All the mus - cles tight - en in her face, bu - ries her soul
(3.) on comes the pa - nic light, hold - ing on with fin - gers and feel - ings a - like.
Em7
A
in one em - brace. They're one and the same,
But the time has come to move
G
1° only
D
just like wa - ter.
a - long.
And the fire fades a - way

Bm7
G
Bm/F#
and most of ev - 'ry day is full of tired ex - cu - ses,
Em
A
D
Bm7
but it's too hard to say. I wish it were sim - ple but we give up ea - si - ly.
G
Bm/F#
Em
A
Bm
Bm/A
You're close e - nough to see that you're the oth - er
1.
G
A
D
Dsus2
Dsus4
Dsus2
side of the world to me.
3. And

2.
G
A
Em7
Gmaj7
side of the world.
Can you help me?
Can you let me go?
D
Dsus2
Dsus4
Dsus2
Em7
And can you still love
Bm
A
A/G
F#m
A/E
me when you can't see me an - y - more?
D
Bm7
G
Bm/F#
And the fire fades a - way, most of ev - 'ry day is full of tired ex - cu -

Em
A
D
Bm7
-ses, but it's too hard to say.
I wish it were sim - ple but we give up ea - si-ly.
G
Bm/F♯
Em
A
Bm
Bm/A
You're close e - nough to see that you're the oth-er
G
A
Bm
Bm/A
G
A
side of the world, oh, the oth-er side of the world.
Bm
Bm/A
G
A
D
You're the oth-er side of the world to me.

Only Hope

Words & Music by Jonathan Foreman

E/B
A5(add9)
E5
A5(add9)
G♯7(omit 3/5)
C♯m7
4fr
in - fi-nite cold;
dreams are so far,
but you sing to me
sing to me of the
E/B
A5(add9)
E5
A5(add9)
G♯7(omit 3/5)
ov - er and ov - er and ov - er a - gain.
plans that you have for me ov - er a - gain.
So I
C♯
4fr
G♯/C♯
4fr
F♯add9
lay my
(3°) So I lay my
head back down,
and I
C♯
4fr
G♯/C♯
4fr
F♯add9
G♯/A♯
F♯/A♯
G♯/A♯
A♯m
lift my hands and pray to be on - ly yours, I

Play twice at 𝄋
F♯add9
G♯/A♯ F♯/A♯ G♯/A♯ A♯m
A
5fr
G♯sus4
4fr
G♯7sus4
4fr
To Coda 𝄌
pray to be on - ly yours; I know now_you're my on - ly
1. C♯5(add9)
4fr
C♯m/E
4fr
Amaj7
5fr
G♯sus4
4fr
G♯
4fr
hope.
2. C♯5
4fr
B
G♯m/C♯
4fr
C♯m
4fr
hope.
3
I give you my_ des - ti - ny,
B
G♯m/C♯
4fr
C♯m
4fr
B
C♯sus4(add9)
G♯7/B♯
C♯m
4fr
I'm giv - ing you all of me.
I want your_ sym-pho - ny.

D♯ D♯/C♯ G♯/B♯ G♯ F♯add9 F♯
6fr
4fr
Sing - ing in all that I am, at the top of my lungs,
G♯ F♯add9 F♯ F♯/E♯ D♯m7 G♯7sus4
4fr
D.S. al Coda
I'm giv - ing it back.
Coda
G♯sus4 G♯7sus4 C♯m7 C♯m/E C♯m7/G♯ C♯m7 A5 E
on - ly hope.
A G♯ C♯m7 C♯m/E C♯m7/G♯ C♯m7 A5 E A G♯7 C♯m
5fr
rit.
Hmm, hmm. Ooh.

Proud

Words & Music by Peter John Vettese & Heather Small

G
Bm
Em7
I step
(2.) So I step
out of the or-di-na-ry,
I can feel my
D/F♯
G
D/A
G/B
soul as-cend-ing,
I'm on my way, can't stop me now:
And you can do the
A7sus4
C/D
G/D
D
Em/D
D
3fr
same, yeah.
What have you done to-day to make you feel proud?
C/D
G/D
D
Em/D
D
It's nev-er too late to try.
What have you done to-day to make you feel proud?

Em
Bm
G
Hmm, hmm. You could be so man - y peo - ple if you make that
E/G♯
4fr
C
G
to Coda
N.C.
break for free - dom. What have you done to - day to make you feel proud?
B5
A5
E5
B5
A5
E5
2. Still so man - y an - swers I don't know. (There are so man - y an -

B5
A5
E5
D.S. al Coda
- swers.) Real - ise that to ques - tion is how we grow
(To ques - tion is to grow.)
Coda
Bm
E
E7
G
proud? Yeah! We need a change Yeah! Do it to - day! Yeah!
3
D
G/D
Em/D
D
Bm
E
E7
I can feel my spi - rit ri - sing. Change! Yeah! We need a change, yeah! So do it to -
C
G
C/D
- day! Yeah! 'Cos I can see a clear ho - ri - zon.

G/D
D
Em/D
D
3fr
To make you feel proud yeah!
Let me hear ya, let me hear ya, let me
C/D
G/D
D
Em/D
D
3fr
hear ya! So what have you done to - day to make you feel proud?
Em7
Bm
G
3
Yeah, yeah, yeah.
'Cos you could be so man - y peo - ple
if you make that
E/G#
4fr
C
G
break for free - dom.
So what have you done to - day to make you feel

C/D
G/D
D
Em/D
D
proud? What have you done to - day? Let me hear ya! What have you done to - day?
C/D
G/D
D
Em/D
D
What have you done to - day? What have you done to - day to make you feel proud? Whoa,
Em7
Bm
G
yeah, yeah, yeah, yeah. You could be so man - y peo - ple. Just make that
E/G♯
C
G
N.C.
break for free - dom: So, what have you done to - day to make you feel proud?
8vb

Out Of The Blue

Words & Music by Delta Goodrem & Guy Chambers

C♭sus2
B♭m
I had - n't giv - en up; just thought I'd be walk - ing
G♭
A♭sus4
4fr
A
C♯m/G♯
4fr
the world a - lone. Out of the blue, there I met you;
F♯m
D
D/E
showed me a life I can't see with - out you.
A
C♯m
4fr
F♯m
A/E
And there's just no way that I can fight these e - mo - tions, your

Bsus4
2fr
B
Bsus4
2fr
B
en - er - gy run - ning through me.
No - bo - dy can re - new me like
E
D
C♯m
4fr
Bm
you. Out of the blue:
can this be true?
F♯
G♭
G♭maj7
Fam-'ly and friends, they were my life,
I was - n't one for but - ter - flies; but

G♭7
G♭maj7
you give me love that I can't dis - guise.
G♭
G♭maj7
There will be times when we're a - part, I want you to know you're in my heart,
G♭7
To Coda
G♭maj7
D♭
4fr
grow-ing in-to a beau - ti - ful gar - den.
No e- mo - tions,
C♭sus2
B♭m
my whole bo - dy felt like ice; need-ed to feel that the

G♭
A♭sus4
4fr
D♭
4fr
sun would shine my way.
My world had turned to dust but I
C♭/E♭
B♭m
had my faith and trust;
just thought I'd be walk - ing
A
B
G♭
D.S. al Coda
the world a - lone.
Coda
G♭maj7
A
C♯m/G♯
4fr
- - den.
Out of the blue, there I met you;

F♯m
D
D/E
I can't be - lieve that this hap - pened so soon.
A
C♯m7
4fr
And there's just no way that I can fight
F♯m
A/E
Bsus4
B
these e - mo - tions, your en - er - gy run - ning through me.
G♭
G♭maj7
G♭7
(Out of the blue there I met you, showed me a life

G♭maj7
G♭
I can't see with - out you)
There will be times when we're a - part, I
G♭maj7
G♭7
G♭maj7
want you to know you're in my heart, grow-ing in-to a beau - ti - ful gar - den.
G♭
G♭maj7
G♭7
(Out of the blue there I met you, showed me a life
1, 2.
3.
G♭maj7
G♭maj7
G♭
I can't see with - out you)
I can't see with - out you.)

Shiver

Words & Music by Natalie Imbruglia, Francis White & Shepard Soloman

C
G/B
Em7
G
Jump the tracks, can't get back; I don't know an - y - one 'round here,
In a rush, nev - er trust you'll be there; if I'd on - ly stop
C
G/B
Em
but I'm safe this time. 'Cos when you
and take my time. 'Cos with you
F
tell me, tell me, tell me stu - pid things
I'm run - ning, run - ning, run - ning some - where I
C/G
Em/G
F
like you do, yes, I
can't get to. Yes, I

C/G
have to, have to, have to change the rules; I can't lose.
have to, have to, have to change the rules; I'm with you.
G
C
G/B
Em7
G
C
'Cos I shi - ver, I just break up; when I'm near
G/B
Em
G
C
you, it all gets out of hand. Yes, I shi -
G/B
Em7
G
C
- ver, I get pent up; there's no way

To Coda
G/B
Em
1.
F
that I know you'll un - der - stand.
Fadd9
2.
F
C/B♭
What if you get off
Am6
at the next stop?
Would you just wave
Fm6/A♭
6fr
as I'm drift - ing off?
And if I nev - er saw

C/G
Fadd9
C/G
you a - gain, could I
keep hold
of this
Am7
Fadd9
D.S. al Coda
in - side?
'Cos I shi -
Coda
G
C
G/B
Em7
I shi - ver,
D.S. to fade
G
C
G/B
Em
G
C
I shi - ver.
Yes, I shiv -

Say My Name

Words & Music by Rodney Jerkins, Fred Jerkins III, LaShawn Daniels, Beyoncé Knowles, LeToya Luckett, Kelendria Rowland & LaTavia Roberson

B♭9sus4
G7/B
Cm
A♭
"Ba - by", why the sud-den change? Say my name, say my name. If no-one is a -
Fm
B♭9sus4
B dim7
Cm
-round you, say, "Ba-by, I love you," if you ain't run-nin' game. Say my name, say my
A♭
Fm7
B♭9sus4
G7/B
name. You act-ing kind-a sha - dy ain't call-ing me "Ba - by", bet-ter say my
Cm
A♭
Fm
1. An - y oth - er day I would call, you would say, "Ba-by how's your day?" But to -
name.
(Verse 2 see block lyric, Verse 3 Instrumental till *)
fr3
fr4

B♭9sus4
B dim7
Cm
fr3
- day it ain't the same. Ev - 'ry oth - er word is "Uh -
A♭
fr4
Fm
- huh, yeah O. K." Could it be that you are at the
B♭9sus4
B dim7
Cm
fr3
crib with a - no - ther la - dy? If you took it there, first of
A♭
fr4
Fm
all let me say, I am not the one to sit a -

Bb9sus4
Bdim7
Cm
Ab
-round and be played. So prove your-self to me, or the girl that you claim. Why
Fm
don't you say the things that you said to me yes - ter - day? I
Know you say that I am as-sum-ing things. Some-thin's go-in' down, that's the way it seems.
Should-n't be no rea-son why you act - ed strange. No - bo-dy's hold-ing you back from me. 'Cos

Cm
fr3
A♭
fr4
I know how you us - 'ally do. Why you say-in' ev-'ry-thing to me times two?
Fm
B♭9sus4
G7
Why can't you just tell the truth? If some-bo-dy's there then tell me who.
Cm
fr3
A♭
fr4
Fm
Say my name, say my name. If no-one is a - round you, say, "Ba-by, I
B♭9sus4
B dim7
Cm
fr3
love you," if you ain't run - nin' game. Say my name, say my

A♭
fr4
Fm
name. You act - ing kind - a sha - dy ain't call - ing me
B♭9sus4
G7/B
Cm
fr3
A♭
fr4
"Ba - by", why the sud-den change? Say my name, say my name. If no-one is a -
Fm
B♭9sus4
B dim7
Cm
fr3
- round you, say, "Ba - by, I love you," if you ain't run-nin' game. Say my name, say my
A♭
fr4
Fm
1, 2.
B♭9sus4
G7/B
name. You act - ing kind - a sha - dy ain't call - ing me "Ba - by", bet - ter say my

3.
B♭9sus4 G7/B Cm A♭
"Ba - by", bet - ter say my name. Say my name, say my name. If no - one is a -
Fm B♭9sus4 G7/B Cm
- round you, say, "Ba - by, I love you," if you ain't run - nin' game. Say my name, say my
A♭ Fm B♭9sus4 Bdim7
name. You act - ing kind - a sha - dy ain't call - ing me "Ba - by", why the sud - den
Cm A♭ Fm
change? Say my name, say my name. If no - one is a - round you, say, "Ba - by, I

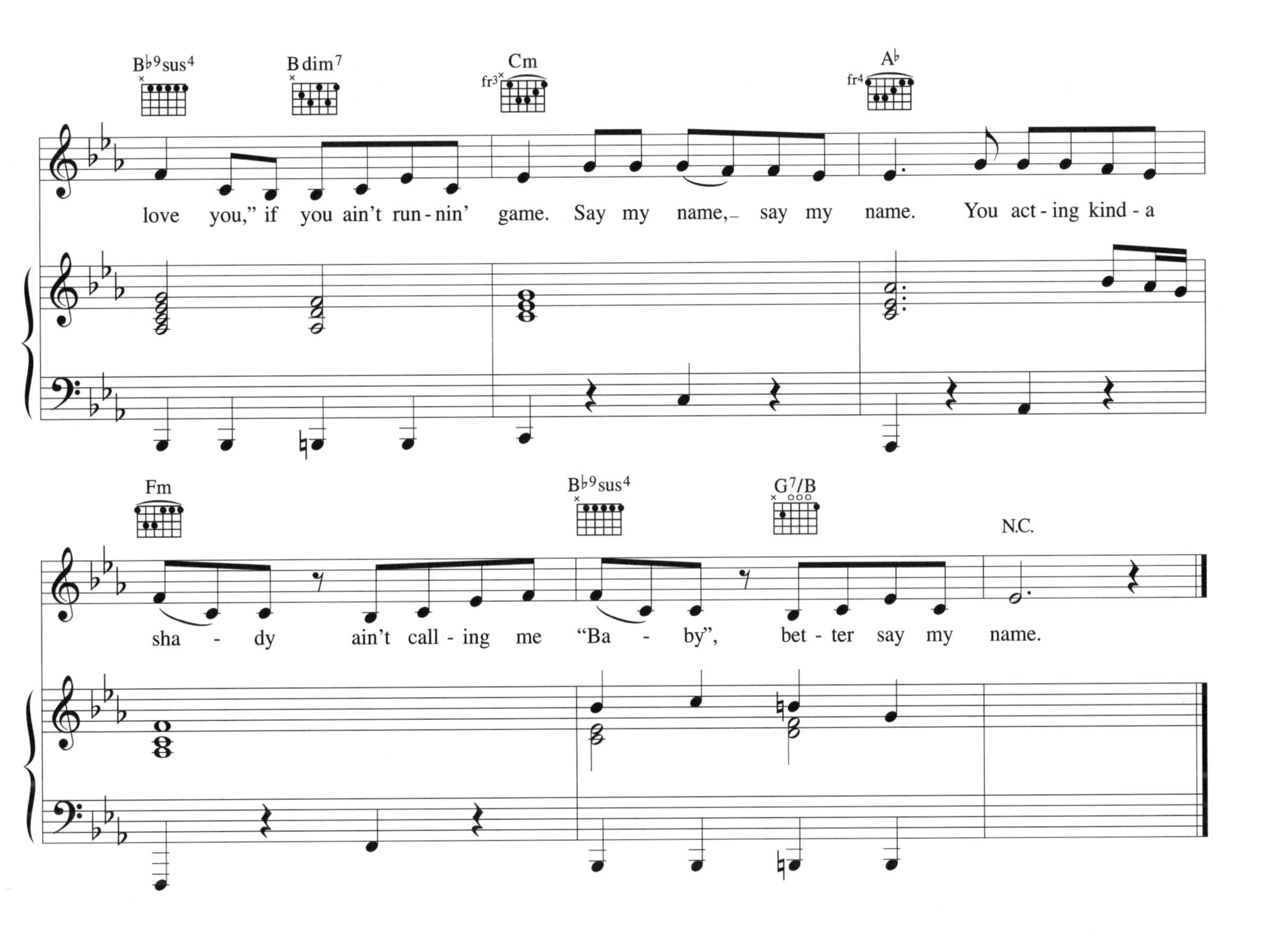

Verse 2:
What is up with this?
Tell the truth, who you with?
How would you like it if
I came over with my clique?
Don't try to change it now,
See you gotta bounce
When two seconds ago
Said you just got in the house.
It's hard to believe that you
Are at home, by yourself
When I just heard the voice,
Heard the voice of someone else.
Just this question:
Why do you feel you gotta lie?
Gettin' caught up in your game,
When you can not say my name.

I know you say that I am assuming things *etc.*

Since U Been Gone

Words & Music by Martin Sandberg & Lukasz Gottwald

G
Am
3fr
E5
2. You're de - di - ca - ted, you took the time.
Was-n't long till I
3. How can I put it? You put me on.
I ev - en fell for that
F(♭5)
F
called you mine.
Yeah, yeah.
Since U been gone.
stu - pid love song.
Yeah, yeah.
Since U been gone.
And all you'd ev - er
hear me say
How come I'd nev - er
hear you say,
is how I pic - ture me with you.
That's all you'd ev - er
"I just wan - na be with you"?
Guess you nev - er

G
N.C.
Bm
Csus2
G
hear me say.
felt that way.
But since U been gone
Bm
Csus2
G
I can breathe for the first time.
I'm so mov-ing on
Em
Csus2
G
Am
yeah, yeah.
Thanks to you
now I get
Em
D/F#
A5
what I want.
Since U been gone.

1.
2.
G
Csus2
You had your chance,
Em
you blew it.
Out of sight,
out of mind.
Shut your mouth
I just can't take it.
A-gain and a-gain
and a-gain and a-gain.
N.C.

Bm
Csus2
G
Since U been gone
2° lead vocal ad lib.
Bm
Csus2
G
I can breathe for the first time. I'm so mov-ing on
Em
Csus2
G
Am
yeah, yeah. Thanks to you now I get,

1.
2.
Em
Am
I get what I want
you should know
that I get,
D/F♯
Am7
I get what I want.
G
Since U been gone.
Since U been gone.
N.C.
Since U been gone.

They

Written by Jem Griffiths & Gerard Young
Incorporating elements from 'Prelude in F Minor'
by J.S. Bach & Ward Swingle

Fm
C7
3fr
be - lieve them to be true. Don't care to think them through.
is act on what they say and then it is that way.
Bbm7
Eb
6fr
Abmaj7
4fr
I'm sor - ry, so sor - ry. I'm sor - ry it's like this.
I'm sor - ry, so sor - ry. I'm sor - ry we do this.
Who are_ they, where are_ they? How can_ they pos - si - bly know all this?

Fm
C7
3fr
Who are — they,
where are — they?
How can — they
pos - si - bly know all this?
C
Fm/C
Csus4/2
Fm
Bb7
Do you see
what I see?
Why do we
live like this?
Is it be - cause it's true
that ig - no - rance is bliss?

Fm B♭m7 E♭ A♭maj7 Fm B♭m7 C7 Fm
6fr 4fr 3fr
Who are they, where are they? How do they know all this?
Fm B♭m7 E♭ A♭maj7 Fm B♭m7 C7 Fm
6fr 4fr 3fr
I'm sor - ry, so sor - ry. I'm sor - ry
it's like this.
we do this.
Fm C C7 Fm B♭m7 C7 Fm
3fr 3fr 3fr
C C7 Fm B♭m7 Bdim7 C
3fr 3fr 3fr

We Belong Together

Words & Music by Mariah Carey, Jermaine Dupri, Kenneth Edmonds,
Manuel Seal, Bobby Womack, Darnell Bristol, Sidney Johnson,
Johnta Austin, Patrick Moten & Sandra Sully

Fmaj7
8fr
G
10fr
1. I did - n't mean it when I said I did - n't love you so.
(2.) sleep at night when you are on my mind, Bob - by
Em7
7fr
F
8fr
I should - 've held on tight, I nev - er should - 've let you go.
Wo - mack's on the ra - di - o say - ing to me "If you
Fmaj7
8fr
G
10fr
I did - n't know no - thing, I was stu - pid I was fool - ish, I was
think you're lone - ly now"... Wait a min - ute this is
Em7
7fr
F
8fr
Fmaj7
8fr
G
10fr
ly - ing to my - self.
I could not fa-thom I would ev - er be with - out your love.
too deep, (too deep) I got - ta change the sta - tion. So I turn the dial try - ing to catch a break and

Em7
7fr
F
8fr
Nev - er i - ma - gine I'd be sit - ting here be - side my - self.
then I hear Ba - by - face. I on - ly
Fmaj7
8fr
G
10fr
'Cos I did - n't know you, 'cos I did - n't know me, but I thought I knew ev - 'ry - thing
think of you and it's break - ing my heart. I'm try - ing to
Em7
7fr
F
8fr
I nev - er felt.
keep it to - geth - er but I'm fall - ing a - part. I'm feel - ing
Fmaj7
8fr
G
10fr
The feel - ing that I'm feel - ing now that I don't hear your voice
all out of my e - le - ment throw - ing things, cry - ing, try - ing to

Em7
7fr
F
8fr
or have your touch and kiss your lips 'cos I don't have a choice.
fi - gure out where the hell I went wrong, the pain re - flect - ed in this
Fmaj7
8fr
G
10fr
Oh, what I would - n't give to have you ly - ing by my side,
song ain't ev - en half of what I'm feel - ing in - side. I need you,
Em7
F
Fmaj7
G
right here,__ 'cos ba - by...
need you back in my life, ba - by...
When you left I lost a part of__
me.__ It's still so hard to be - lieve. Come back ba - by please, 'cos

Em7
F
Fmaj7
G
we be-long_ to-geth-er. Who else am I gon-na lean on when times get rough? Who's_ gon-na talk to
me on the phone till the sun comes up? Who's_ gon - na take your
place, there ain't no - bo - dy bet - ter. Oh, ba - by, ba - by
1.
2.
we be-long_ to-geth-er. 2. I can't
we be-long_ to-geth-er.

Fmaj7
G
Em7
F
8fr
10fr
7fr
When you left I lost a part of me. It's still so hard to be - lieve. Come back ba - by please, 'cos we be - long to - geth - er. Who am I gon - na lean on when times get rough? Who's gon - na talk to me till the sun comes up? Who's gon - na take your place, there ain't no - bo - dy bet - ter. Oh, ba - by, ba - by, we be - long to - geth - er.
Repeat ad lib. to fade

What A Girl Wants

Words & Music by Shelly Peiken & Guy Roche

Em7
Am
Em7
Am
-ed so pa-tient-ly while I got it to-geth-er. Huh, while I fig-ured it out,
hide it all from you. But ba-by you knew me bet-ter than I knew my-
Em7
Am
Em7
Am
yeah, yeah. I on-ly looked but I ne-ver touched, 'cos in my heart was a
-self. Love, you... say if you love some-thing let it go, and if it comes back, it's
Dm9
G11
pic-ture of us: hold-ing hands, mak-ing plans and it's luck-y for me you un-
yours, that's how you know it's for keeps, yeah, it's for sure, and you're read-y and will-ing to give
C
Cmaj7
C7
Fmaj7
-der-stand
me more than
what a girl wants, what a girl needs, what-ev-er makes me hap-py sets

Fm7
B♭11
C
you free and I'm thank-ing you for know-ing ex-act-ly what a girl wants,
Cmaj7
C7
Fmaj7
Fm7
what a girl needs, what-ev-er keeps me in your arms, and I'm thank-ing you for
1. B♭11
N.C.
Am
Em7
Am
(What I want is what you got, and what you got is what I want.)
Em7
N.C.
2. B♭maj7
Am7
C13
2. There was a giv-ing it to me, yeah. (What a girl wants, what a girl needs.)

Fmaj9
B♭11
Am7
C13
Some-bo-dy sen - si-tive, cour-ag-eous, sex-y, cool and like__ you.__ (What a girl wants, what a girl needs,
woh,__ oh yeah!) (What a girl wants, what a girl needs.)
B♭9
Dm7
You let a girl know how much__ you care a-bout__ her I__ swear,__ you're the
Eaug
N.C.
one__ who al - ways knew,__ you knew,__ you knew,__ you knew,__ you knew.__

Ooh, oh, I'm thank-ing you for be-ing here
for me.
What a girl wants, what a girl needs, what-ev-er keeps me in your arms.)
What ev-er keeps
me in your arms is what I need
Lead vocal cont. ad lib.
(What a girl wants, what a girl needs, what-ev-er makes
C
Cmaj7
C7
8fr
me hap-py sets you free and I'm thank-ing you
for know-ing ex-act-ly.
for giv-ing it to me.
Fmaj7
Fm7
B♭11
4fr

1.
C
8fr
Cmaj7
8fr
C7
8fr
What a girl wants, what a girl needs, what-ev-er keeps me in
Fmaj7
8fr
Fm7
8fr
B♭11
4fr
your arms, and I'm thank-ing you for giv-ing it. What a girl...)
2.
Am7
5fr
C13
8fr
Fmaj9
7fr
B♭11
4fr
Am7
5fr
C13
8fr
Fmaj9
7fr
B♭11
4fr
Repeat to fade

You're Gonna Make Me Lonesome When You Go

Words & Music by Bob Dylan

E7sus4 E6 E7sus4 Asus2 E5 E6/9
Been shoot - ing in the dark too long;
D5/A E7sus4 E5 Amaj7
when some-thing's not right, it's wrong. You're gon - na make
D5/A Amaj7
To Coda
1, 2. E7sus4 E6 E7sus4
3, 4.
me lone - some when you go.
E11 Amaj7/E
3B. Flow - ers on the hill - side, bloom-ing cra - zy,
(Verse 4B see block lyric)

E11*
9fr
Amaj7/E*
11fr
cri-ckets talk-ing back and forth in rhyme,
B7
11fr
blue ri-ver run-nin' slow
and la-zy:
E
13fr
oh, I could stay
D
11fr
C♯m
9fr
Bm
7fr
D.S. (4°)
D.S. (5°) al Coda
with you for-ev-er and nev-er re-al-ise the time.

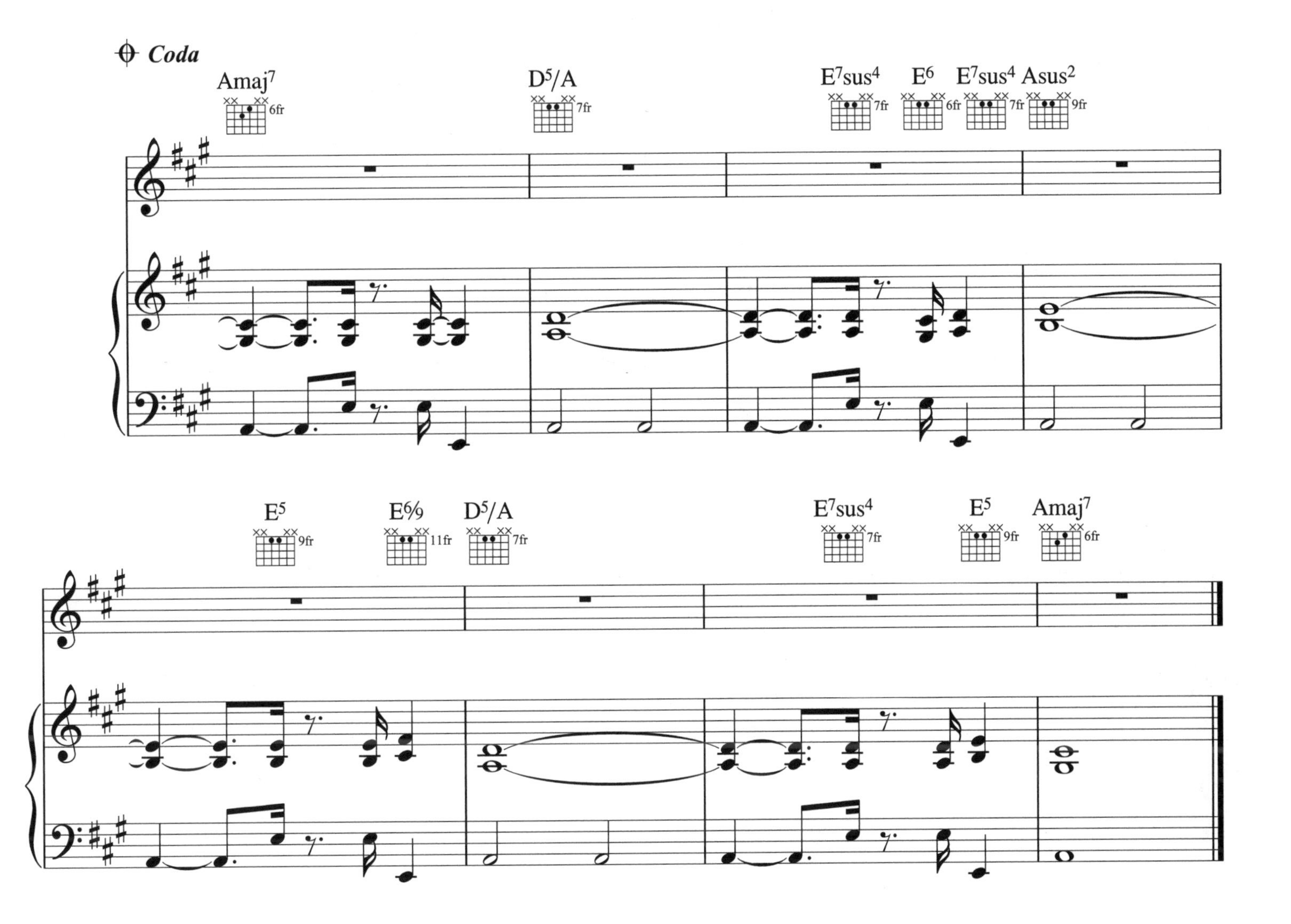

Verse 2:
Dragon clouds so high above,
I've only known careless love,
It's always hit me from below.
This time 'round it's more correct,
Right on target, so direct,
You're gonna make me lonesome when you go.

Verse 3:
Purple clover, Queen Anne lace,
Crimson hair across your face,
You could make me cry if you don't know.
Can't remember what I'm thinking of,
You might be spoiling me too much, love,
You're gonna make me lonesome when you go.

Verse 4:
Situations have ended sad,
Relationships have all been bad,
Mine have been like Verlaine's and Rimbaud.
But there's no way I'd compare
All those scenes to this affair,
You're gonna make me lonesome when you go.

Verse 4B:
You're gonna make me wonder what I'm doing
Staying far behind without you,
You're gonna make me wonder what I'm saying,
Gonna make me give myself a good talking to.

Verse 5:
I'll look for you in old Honolulu,
San Francisco and Ashtabula
You're gonna have to leave me now, I know.
But I'll see you in the skies above,
In the tall grass, in the ones I love,
You're gonna make me lonesome when you go.

Strict Machine

Words & Music by Alison Goldfrap, William Gregory & Nicholas Batt

Won - der - ful e - lec - tric,
F5
B♭5
6fr
won - der - ful e - lec - tric,
F5
B♭5
6fr
won - der - ful e - lec - tric,

A♭5
4fr
G♭5
co - ver me in
F5
N.C.
B♭5
6fr
you.
I'm in love,
I'm in love,
I'm in love with a strict ma - chine.
I'm in love,
I'm in love,
I'm in love with a strict ma - chine.

to Coda
1.
I'm in love,
(on D.S. only)
2. When you send
2. B♭5
6fr
I'm in love,

D.S. al Coda
I'm in love,
Coda
B♭5
6fr
I'm in love,
I'm in love
Vocals 1° only
with a strict mach - ine.
I'm in love,
I'm in love,
Repeat to fade
I'm in love with a strict ma - chine.